ACTION MAN

ANNUAL 2004

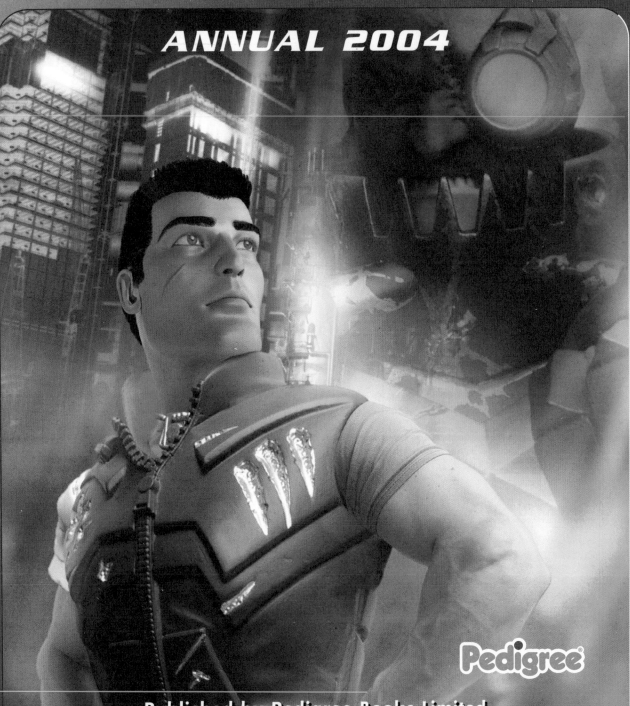

Pedigree

Published by Pedigree Books Limited
Beech Hill House, Walnut Gardens, Exeter, Devon EX4 4DG
E-mail: books@pedigreegroup.co.uk
Published in 2003

£7.50

Profile... ISLAND X

EXTREME MOUNTAIN

X-CITY

MISSION CONTENTS

JUNGLE ZONE

OCEAN ZONE

X'S BASE

ICE ZONE

Profile... ISLAND X

LOWDOWN ON THE ISLAND OF TERROR

THE GREATEST THREAT THE WORLD HAS EVER KNOWN HAS APPEARED IN THE OCEAN. A MYSTERIOUS X-SHAPED ISLAND IS SLOWLY DRIFTING TOWARDS CIVILISATION. SPY SATELLITES SHOW THAT THE ISLAND HAS A DEATH RAY CAPABLE OF WIPING OUT EVERY MAJOR CITY IN A MATTER OF MINUTES! ISLAND X IS KNOWN TO BE THE CREATION OF DR X WHO IS POWER CRAZED AND INTENT ON RULING THE WORLD. MANY ARMIES HAVE TRIED TO DESTROY THIS EVIL PLACE, BUT THEY HAVE ALL FAILED. NOW THERE IS ONLY ONE PERSON WHO CAN BRING THE WORLD BACK FROM THE BRINK OF DISASTER...

ACTION MAN!

OCEAN ZONE

SEETHING WITH DEADLY SHARKS THAT HAVE BEEN GENETICALLY ENGINEERED TO BE EXTRA LARGE AND AGGRESSIVE. NO SWIMMER THAT ENTERS THESE WATERS EVER COMES OUT ALIVE. THE SEABED IS ALSO DOTTED WITH UNDERWATER VOLCANOES THAT DR X HAS THE POWER TO ERUPT AT ANY TIME.

EXTREME MOUNTAIN

A GRIM AND DESOLATE PLACE WHERE NOBODY EVER GOES... EXCEPT THE POLAR BEARS! THESE HUGE WHITE MONSTERS HAVE BEEN SPECIALLY BRED BY PROFESSOR GANGRENE TO BE DEADLY KILLERS. THIS ZONE ALSO HIDES THE LABORATORY WHERE PROFESSOR GANGRENE CONDUCTS HIS EVIL SCIENTIFIC EXPERIMENTS.

ICE ZONE

Without the right equipment, no one survives for long in the sub-zero temperatures of this white and silent place. It is also the home of Anti-Freeze, an horrific ice monster whose touch freezes human flesh and whose special blood means he does not even feel the cold!

JUNGLE ZONE

Guarded by Dr X's terrifying Aztec warriors. These fierce fighters will attack anyone who comes near their ancient temples and pyramids buried deep in the thick jungle. The buildings are full of gold and jewels...and many unexpected booby traps!

X-CITY

Situated at the heart of the island, X-City is believed to be the location of Dr X's secret base and the Death Ray that threatens the world. The dirty, polluted streets are deserted except for the soldiers and guards that patrol the city's many rings of defences.

MISSION BRIEF

Time is running out! Island X is almost within range of Europe and America. Soon, Dr X will be able to destroy every major city with his Death Ray.
The island is bristling with defences. Approach by sea. This can only be done by stealth.
Land on Island X and prepare for action!

ACTION MAN DOWNLOADS DATA ABOUT ISLAND X VIA A STATE-OF-THE-ART MOBILE PHONE. IT MAKES PICTURE MESSAGING LOOK A THING OF THE PAST – HIS MOBILE PROJECTS A FULL-COLOUR HOLOGRAM IMAGE INTO THE AIR!

OCEAN ZONE

Location –
EAST OF ISLAND X

Nearest zones –
ICE AND JUNGLE

Known Defences -
GENETICALLY ENGINEERED SHARKS,
THE LARGEST AND FIERCEST SINCE
THE TIME OF THE DINOSAURS.

Sea temperature -
15 DEGREES CENTIGRADE

Depth -
UNKNOWN

Special features -
EVIDENCE OF VOLCANIC
ERUPTIONS OF RECENT DATE.

Mission Manta -

* Modelled on the Manta Ray, a gigantic flatfish with wing like fins that grow up to 7 metres wide.

* Made of a special hi-tech alloy that combines aluminium with air molecules. This metal is lightweight, super-strong and able to float easily in water.

* Action Man's mini-sub has a powerful rotary engine surrounded by layers of baffle-boxes. This enables Mission Manta to achieve "silent running" - moving swiftly and noiselessly underwater.

* The illuminated range-finder can be read easily, even in murky water. The digital read-out gives a constantly changing stream of info. about depth, direction and speed. The laser-guided aiming sight cannot be deflected once it has locked onto its target.

* Mission Manta has twin missile launchers located in its "horns". These open to fire two high-speed underwater rockets capable of blowing a huge hole in any ship. The missiles are sonar controlled and have never been known to miss their target.

* Action Man wears Scuba diving gear when deploying his special underwater vehicle. He needs extra oxygen supplies to cope with the speed at which it pulls him along underwater.

'WHICH DIRECTION?' PUZZLE

Requesting Mission Assistance

ACTION MAN'S FIRST MISSION IS TO LAND ON ISLAND X...BUT WHICH DIRECTION SHOULD HE COME FROM? HELP ACTION MAN BY FINDING THE VITAL INFORMATION HIDDEN IN THIS PUZZLE.

ALL THESE WORDS HAVE SOMETHING TO DO WITH THE OCEAN. FIND THEM IN THE GRID AND CROSS THEM OUT. THEY ARE SPELT IN ALL DIRECTIONS INCLUDING BACKWARDS. WHEN YOU HAVE FINISHED, THERE WILL BE FOUR LETTERS LEFT.

TRANSFER THESE LETTERS, IN ORDER FROM THE TOP, TO THE BOX UNDERNEATH THE GRID. THEY WILL SPELL OUT THE DIRECTION FROM WHICH ACTION MAN SHOULD APPROACH ISLAND X.

Thanks for your help!

W	A	V	E	S	S	S
A	H	E	E	L	S	S
T	E	A	L	A	A	A
E	A	E	L	S	N	N
R	H	T	T	T	E	D
S	T	I	D	E	S	S

TIDES
WAVES
SALT
WHALES
SAND
EELS
SHELLS
WATER

Action Man should approach Island X from the...

☐ ☐ ☐ ☐

14

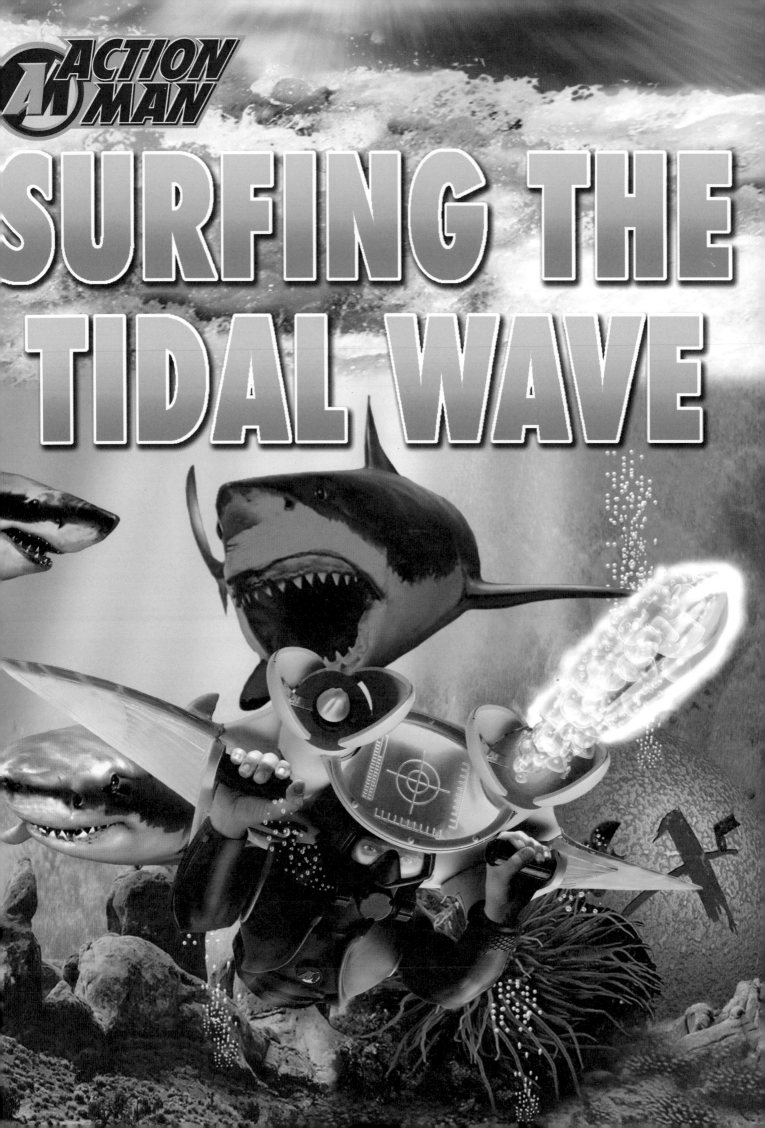

SQUEEZING EVERY DROP OF SPEED FROM HIS MANTA MISSION, ACTION MAN BEGAN A DEADLY UNDERWATER RACE...

NEED TO GO EVEN FASTER - THE BRUTE'S GAINING ON ME!

ARRGH! MY WAY'S COMPLETELY BLOCKED

THE ONLY WAY WAS UP! WITH THE SHARK SNAPPING AT HIS FLIPPERS, ACTION MAN BROKE THE SURFACE...

HEY! THIS WALL OF ROCK IS A TINY ISLAND!

Profile... ACTION MAN

Not much is known about Action Man, except that he is The Greatest Hero of Them All! This cloak of secrecy prevents his enemies from using personal information against him. What can be revealed is this...

Distinguishing Features

* Scar on right cheek
* Tattoo on left arm.

Attitudes and Abilities

* Very focused - nothing distracts him from completing each mission.
* Fearless in the face of danger.
* Extremely fit and strong.
* Highly intelligent and able to adapt to any situation.
* Good sense of humour, especially at moments of great peril.

Special Skills

Achieved 100% success rate in all of the following –

* Survival Skills
* Unarmed combat
* Flying skills
* Communication

Special Power

Action Man is always one step ahead of the game. So he can tackle even the greatest threats single handed!

Action Man believes in taking action to defeat evil and his goal in life is to rid the world of Dr X once and for all.

MISSION BRIEF

On Island X, you must track down Dr X and find his base. To get in, you will need a special key that is protected by a secret code. To crack this code, you must find certain items along the way.

The first item is in the Jungle Zone. It's the hardest natural substance in the world. For security reasons, that's all you can be told.

JUNGLE ZONE

Location -
COVERS THE ENTIRE NORTH EASTERN TIP OF ISLAND X.

Nearest zones -
VOLCANO AND EXTREME MOUNTAIN.

Known Defences -
INHABITED BY FIERCE JUNGLE WARRIORS DESCENDED FROM THE AZTECS OF ANCIENT MEXICO, CAPTURED AND TRAINED BY DR X.

Temperature -
A SEARING 30 DEGREES CELSIUS.

Humidity -
100%. THIS ZONE IS LIKE A STEAM BATH!

Special features -
AN AZTEC PYRAMID WITH MANY DANGERS AND A HIDDEN SURPRISE.

Jungle Adventure Crossbow

* MADE FROM THE WOOD OF THE JULEPPY, A RARE AND ALMOST EXTINCT TREE THAT GROWS ONLY IN THE AMAZON RAINFORESTS OF SOUTH AMERICA.
* EXTRA LIGHTWEIGHT, TOUGH AND EXTREMELY SPRINGY, JULEPPY WOOD ENABLES THE CROSSBOW TO FIRE AT AN ASTONISHING 130 MPH.
* THE RANGE OF THE WEAPON IS 275 METRES.
* THE CROSSBOW FIRES DARTS WHICH HAVE SUCTION DISKS ON THE END. THESE DISKS ARE COATED WITH A SPECIAL GLUE. WHEN THE DARTS HIT SOMETHING, THEY STICK...AND STICK FAST!
* A CUSTOMISED ARM GRIP ALLOWS ACTION MAN TO HOLD THE CROSSBOW AS STEADY AS A ROCK WHEN AIMING AND FIRING.
* SPECIAL ONE-PULL ADJUSTABLE STRAP ALLOWS CROSSBOW TO BE CARRIED ACROSS THE SHOULDERS, LEAVING BOTH HANDS FREE TO COPE WITH THE THICK JUNGLE VEGETATION.

CLARIFY SEARCH PUZZLE

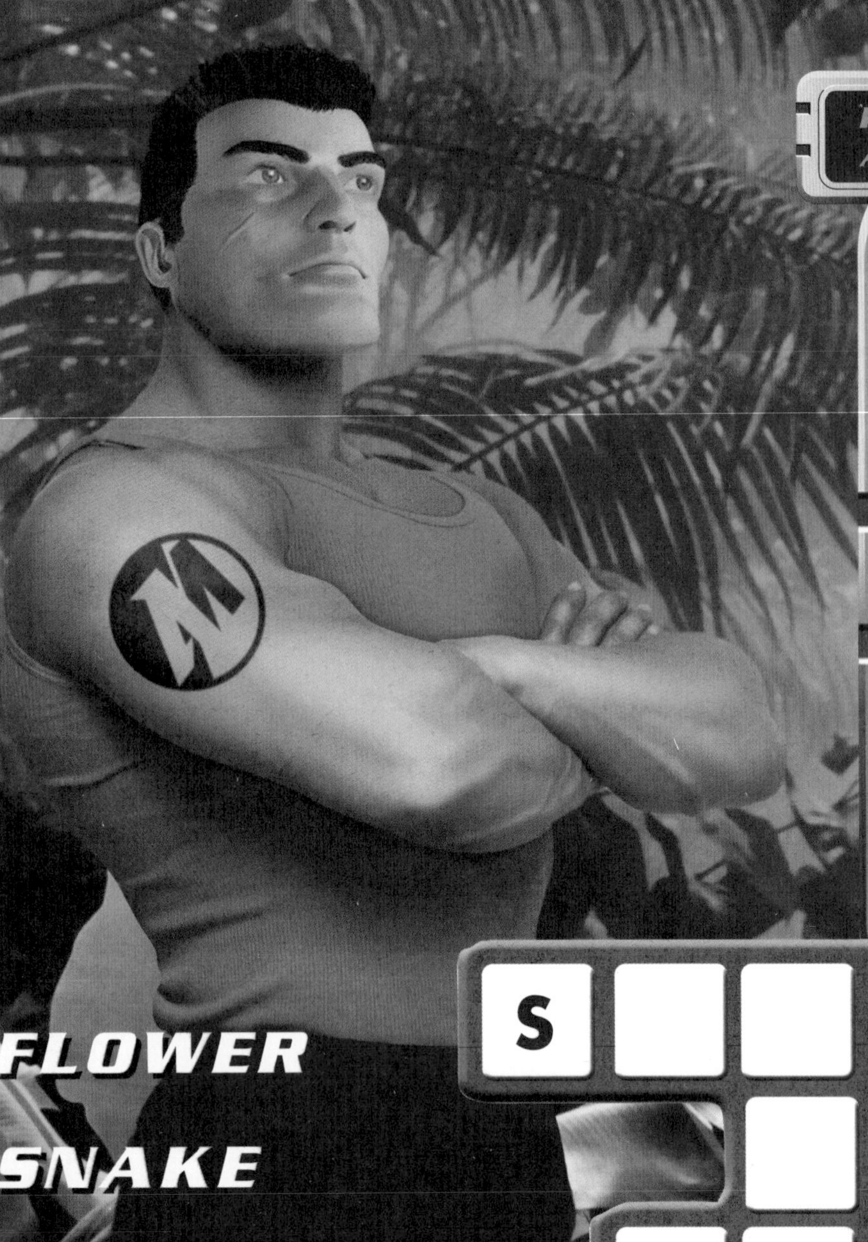

Requesting Mission Assistance!

"THE HARDEST NATURAL SUBSTANCE IN THE WORLD!" WHAT EXACTLY IS ACTION MAN LOOKING FOR IN THE JUNGLE ZONE?
HELP TO NARROW THE SEARCH BY SOLVING THIS PUZZLE. ALL THE WORDS BELOW HAVE SOMETHING TO DO WITH THE JUNGLE. FIT THEM INTO THE GRID, USING THE LETTERS ALREADY IN PLACE TO GUIDE YOU.
WHEN YOU HAVE FINISHED, THE MIDDLE SECTION - READING DOWNWARDS - WILL REVEAL THE OBJECT OF HIS SEARCH.

FLOWER
SNAKE
BIRDS
RIVER
TEMPLE
SPIDER
MONKEY

S						
						R
		N				
				P		
					E	
	M					
		R				

Answer: Action Man is looking for a DIAMOND

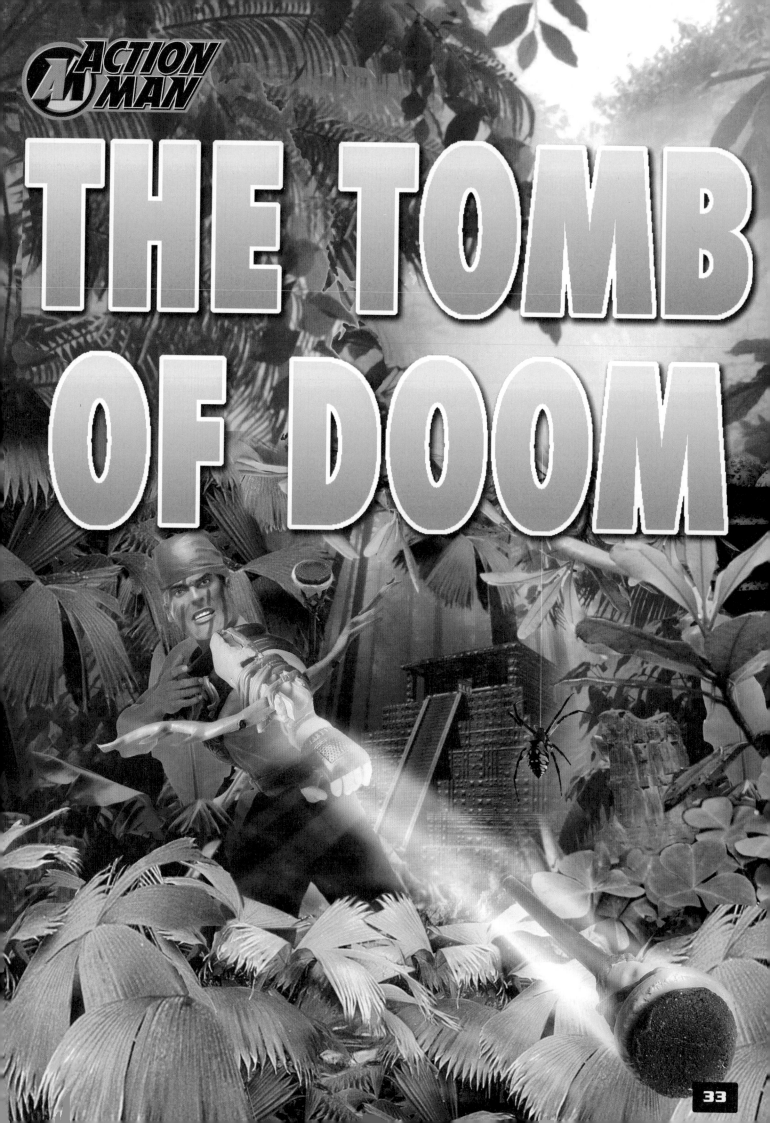

THE TOMB OF DOOM

HIDING HIS ISLAND X RACER, ACTION MAN MADE HIS WAY DEEPER INTO THE JUNGLE ON FOOT...

HMM! HUMAN FOOTPRINTS AND RAPTOR TRACKS. THIS PATH MUST LEAD TO SOMETHING THEY'RE PROTECTING!

SURE ENOUGH, THE TRAIL LED ACTION MAN TO AN ANCIENT AZTEC PYRAMID HIDDEN DEEP IN THE JUNGLE...

GEE! WHAT AN EVIL LOOKING PLACE!

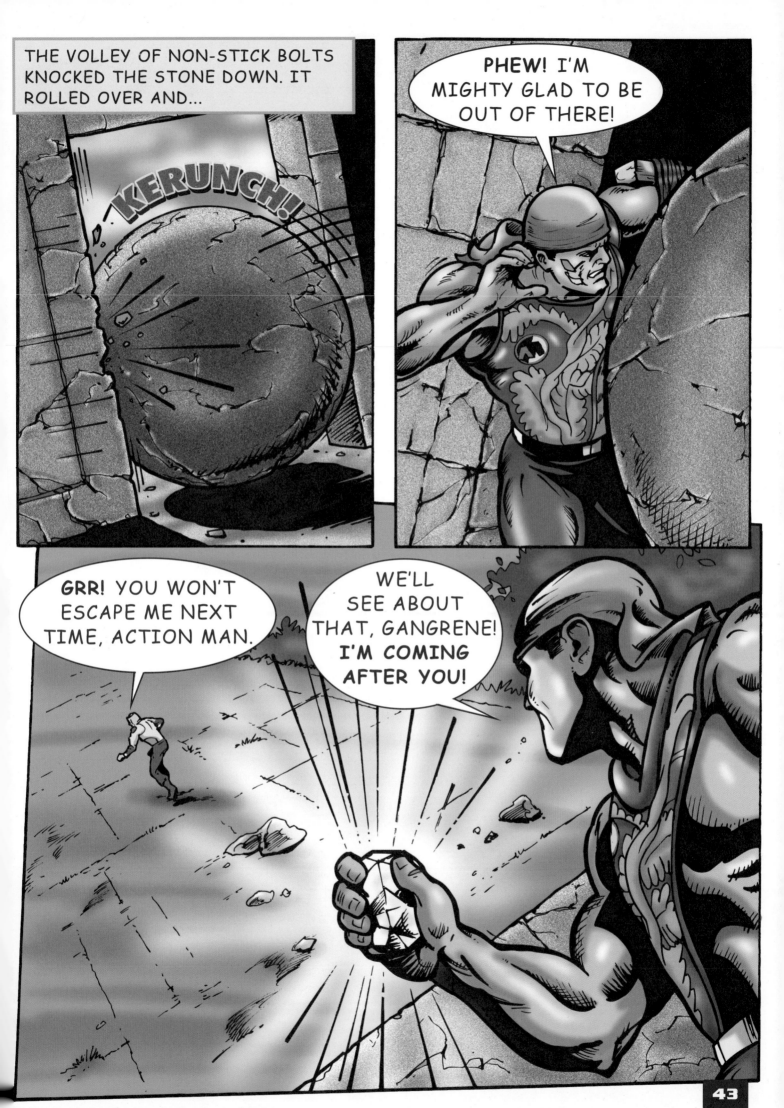

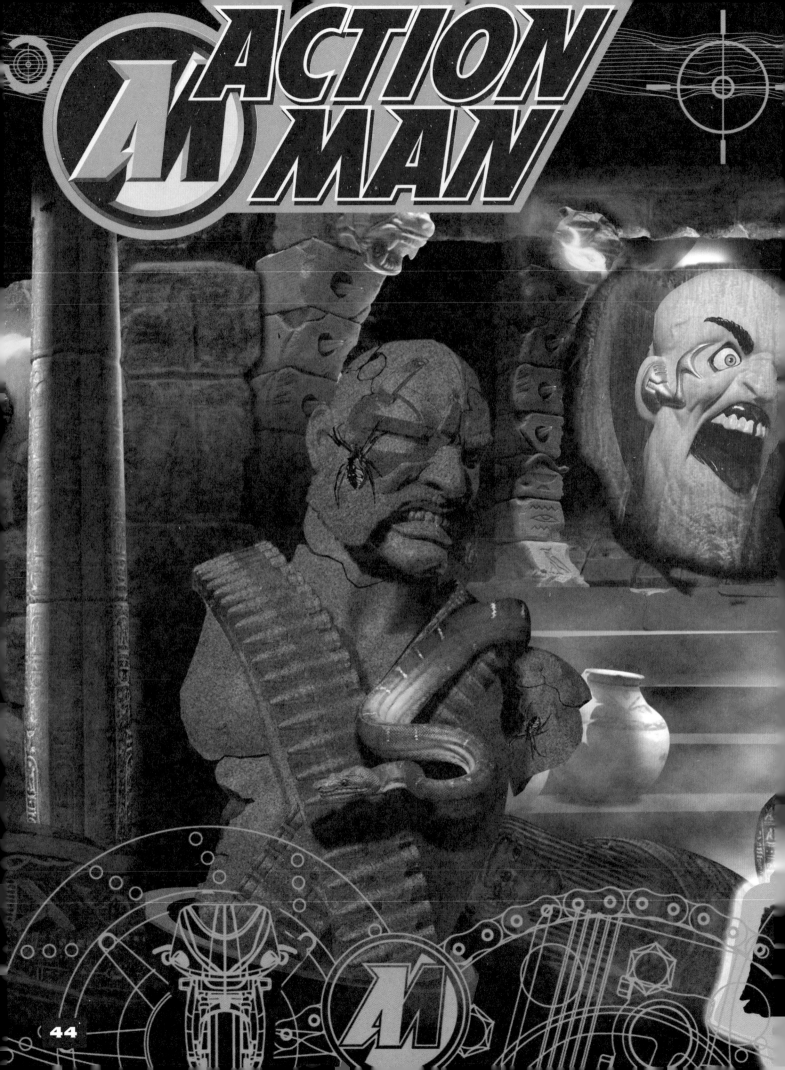

PYRAMID MISSION

Profile... DR. X

The evil Doctor has been Public Enemy Number One for a long time, only prevented from conquering the world by the heroic deeds of Action Man. Now he has reinvented himself and is more cruel and deadly than ever before...

BACKGROUND

Dr X has one simple ambition - to rule the world. He is cruel, cowardly and cunning, always thinking up new ways to achieve his terrible goal. He also has the ability to reinvent himself from time to time, adding new and ever more powerful destructive powers to his body.

SPECIAL POWERS

The all new Dr X has these weapons built into his body...

* Whiplash Hair

Every strand of the doctor's dreadlocks has been strengthened with trilithium. One swing of his head, Dr X can slice through concrete like butter!

* Bionic Arm

His up-graded metal arm is now made of high-strength, lightweight super-steel! It can crush anything in it's grip and smash through the thickest walls with a single blow.

* X-Ray Eye

This special power is the work of Dr X's partner-in-crime, Professor Gangrene. The new, improved lens has a built-in X-ray system that allows the Doctor to see through anything.

* Built-In Weapons

A hidden chest cavity houses two high-powered rocket launchers. They are Dr X's most deadly threat! Fired in less than a second, they can destroy anything in their path.

Dr X will not rest until he has achieved his goal of world domination. We can only hope that Action Man has the power to stop him!

MISSION BRIEF

You must now track
Professor Gangrene up
Extreme Mountain.
Great danger lurks
on the lower slopes, so
beware of being
ambushed.
You have the diamond.
At the top of the
mountain, you must
exchange this for a
mysterious glowing
rock. The location of the
rock is the home of
early Man. That is all
you can be told for
security reasons.
End transmission.

EXTREME MOUNTAIN

Height -
UNKNOWN. ESTIMATE FROM SPY SATELLITES APPROX. 2500 METRES

Nearest zones -
VOLCANO ZONE AND X CITY

Known defenses -
THE LOWER SLOPES ARE THE TERRITORY OF A PACK OF VICIOUS RAPTOR DINOSAURS THAT USE THIS AREA AS THEIR HUNTING GROUND.

Temperature -
SATELLITE ESTIMATES SUGGEST ABOUT 8 DEGREES CELSIUS ON THE LOWER SLOPES, DROPPING TO A CHILLY MINUS 5 DEGREES CELSIUS NEAR THE SUMMIT.

Special features -
NOT KNOWN. NOBODY HAS EVER GOT PAST THE RAPTORS ON THE LOWER SLOPES! HOWEVER, A SCIENTIST WHO FLED THE ISLAND TO ESCAPE DR X'S CONSTANT BULLYING REPORTS SIGHTINGS OF RARE WILD ANIMALS ON THE HIGHER SLOPES.

MISSION DATA-EQUIPMENT

Altitude Attack -

* Employs the latest state-of-the-art parachute technology, based on a 400 year old design by world-famous artist and scientific genius, Leonardo da Vinci.
* Made of ultra lightweight nylon material and sewn together in panels, giving extra strength and confining any holes, tears in the material to just a small section of the parachute.
* The ripcord, which opens the parachute, is fitted with an automatic timing device. So the Altitude Attack opens by itself, leaving Action Man free to cope with any possible threats from the air or the ground.
* Strong, lightweight harness transmits info. about speed and wind-force to Action Man's body, thus combining safety with extreme comfort.
* Controls handles either side allow the chute to be flown like a hand-glider, avoiding enemy fire and allowing for a nimble, two-footed landing.
* Camouflage pattern on canopy prevents Altitude Attack being spotted from above and disguises it amidst the trees of a thickly wooded area.

Snowboard Extreme

* STREAMLINED SHAPE GIVES MAXIMUM SPEED ON DOWNHILL RUNS.
* LIGHTWEIGHT DESIGN ALLOWS FOR QUICK TURNS IN DEEP SNOW.
* SPECIAL DUO-FINS ON EITHER SIDE MAKE THE SNOWBOARD EXTREMELY STABLE, EVEN ON THE MOST SLIPPERY ICE.
* CIRCULAR GRIPPER PADS MADE OF POWDERED GRAPHITE PREVENT FEET FROM SLIPPING OFF BOARD.
* BUILT-IN WEAPON - HIGH POWERED SNOW DISCS. WHEN FIRED FROM THE FRONT OF THE SNOWBOARD, THESE SPINNING DISCS PICK UP SPEED AND CAN STUN AN ENEMY EVEN AT A GREAT DISTANCE.

EXACT LOCATION PUZZLE

EXTREME MOUNTAIN IS A BIG PLACE AND ACTION MAN CAN'T AFFORD TO WASTE ANY TIME.
CAN YOU HELP HIM TO PINPOINT EXACTLY WHERE TO FIND THE MYSTERIOUS GLOWING ROCK?
THE WORDS IN THE JUMBLE ARE ALL TO DO WITH CLIMBING MOUNTAINS. ONE HAS TEN LETTERS, ONE HAS NINE LETTERS...AND SO ON UP TO THREE LETTERS.
BY COUNTING THE LETTERS OF EACH WORD, AND USING THE LETTERS ALREADY IN THE GRID TO GUIDE YOU, FIT THE WORDS INTO THE RIGHT LEVEL OF THE WORD MOUNTAIN.
WHEN YOU HAVE FINISHED, THERE WILL BE ONE WORD LEFT OVER. THIS IS WHAT ACTION MAN MUST FIND AT THE TOP OF EXTREME MOUNTAIN.

ROPES
SAFETYROPE
ICE
SNOWICE
BASECAMP
CAVE
FOOTHILLS
RAVINE
FLAG

WHAT GOES AROUND, COMES AROUND!

ACTION MAN

Action Man had located his nearest equipment drop and changed into his winter gear. He also had his Altitude Attack strapped to his back. As first light crept above the horizon, he began the long trek up the steep mountain carrying his Snowboard Extreme.

He was following a line of shoe-prints in the snow.

"Clearly, Gangrene went this way," he murmured, " but there's no sign of any polar bear tracks. I reckon I'm safe."

In fact, the terrifying creatures were waiting for Action Man at the top of the first ridge. The huge bears, specially bred by Grangrene to be cunning as well as cruel, had kept to the rocks, knowing that would avoid leaving any footprints in the snow.

"*Three* of them!" gasped Action Man. "This could be tricky!"

The other side of the ridge had a long snow-covered slope that led to the bottom of the next ridge. Action Man decided to outrun the polar bears and leave them behind. So, dodging past their savage jaws, he sped off on his Snowboard Extreme.

It was a good idea...but it did not work out. The bears had specially enlarged pads on their paws that gave them total grip on snow and ice.

"These guys are *fast!*" cried Action Man, looking over his shoulder at the snarling white monsters. "I'm not going to be able to outrun them. I'll have to stand and fight!"

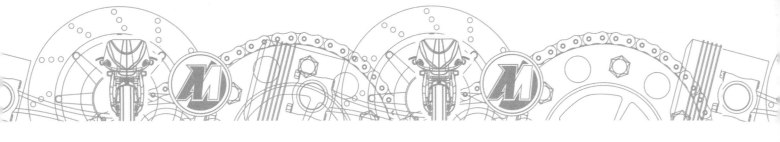

Reaching a stunted tree at the bottom of the slope, Action Man took cover and primed his Snowboard Extreme to act as a weapon.

"Take aim," he said out loud. "FIRE!"

A volley of powerful spinning disks shot out the end of the Snowboard.

The disks flew straight and true, hitting two of the polar bears. The first gave a bellow of pain and loped away out of sight. The second gave a deafening groan and dropped to the ground, stunned. Action Man had only one disk left.

"Where's the third one gone?" he cried.

The answer to his question came too soon for Action Man's liking! The third bear was right behind him! KER-UNNCH! The deadly creature snapped at him with its rows of razor-sharp teeth, narrowly missing his arm and biting the end off the Skateboard Extreme instead.

"That's done it!" gasped Action Man. "My last disk is the shape of a boomerang now!"

Sensing victory, the creature closed in for the kill.

"Desperate times call for desperate measures!" cried Action Man, taking a chance and pointing his Snowboard Extreme into the air.

PHUT! He fired his final damaged disk in the opposite direction to the gnashing white monster.

To anyone watching, it would have seemed like an act of madness. But Action Man reckoned that if his disk was shaped like a boomerang, it would fly like a boomerang. He was right!

WHOOSH! The whirling disk flew round in a circle and headed back towards the polar bear. The bear was looking the other way when it struck, knocking him right off his feet.

"They say what goes around, comes around," laughed Action Man, sprinting off up the next ridge of the mountain. He knew he had got past Gangrene's terrifying polar bears. But he still had to find the hidden cave. And what sort of ordeal awaited him on the upper half of Extreme Mountain?

EQUIPMENT MALFUNCTION PUZZLE

Wherever he goes on Island X, Action Man knows that Dr X is following him. Action Man keeps an eye on his enemy with the use of his high powered digital telescope...but the air pressure on Extreme Mountain is preventing it from working properly. It does not give the same image twice!

Study these two images of Dr X. Can you spot six small differences between them?

COLOURING ACTION

It's hard to tell who is more eager to hunt down Action Man - the polar bears or Professor Gangrene. Colour this exciting scene of Action Man, once again escaping their clutches, with your crayons, felt pens or gel pens.

RAVINE DISASTER PUZZLES

Requesting Mission Assistance!

THIS COULD BE THE END OF THE MISSION AND CURTAINS FOR ACTION MAN! HAVING SHAKEN OFF GANGRENE AND THE RAPTORS, HE FELL OFF HIS SNOWBOARD EXTREME. IT TUMBLED TO THE BOTTOM OF A STEEP RAVINE. HE MUST GET IT BACK!
HELP ACTION MAN TO RETRIEVE HIS VITAL PIECE OF EQUIPMENT BY TRACING THE ONE PATH THAT LEADS THROUGH THE OBSTACLES IN THE ICY RAVINE.

KINGDOM OF THE CAT

Having left the killer bears below, Action Man began the difficult task of climbing the top half of Mountain Extreme. He looked round the empty, snow-covered slopes.

"No sign of a cave yet," he murmured.

By keeping to a steady walk, Action Man made good time. The summit was just coming into view when… SNARL! He found himself face-to-face with a Snow Leopard! The creature looked angry and vicious. Action Man had no choice but to back away down the mountainside.

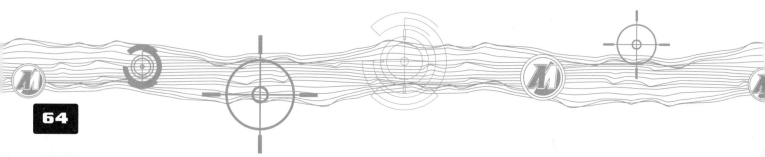

Closing his eyes for a second, Action Man recalled what was stored in his memory bank – Snow Leopard. Proper name: "Ounce". Member of the big cat family. Very rare – only a few left in the wild.

Opening his eyes again, Action Man saw the Ounce limping away.

"No wonder the poor creature's angry," he cried. "There's a steel trap round its leg!"

Action Man knew he had to help this animal. Fitting a special dart to his rifle, he fired at the Snow Leopard and put the creature to sleep for a few minutes. Then, with his bare hands, Action Man pulled the trap apart. He just had time to smear some healing ointment on the wounds before the big cat began to stir.

"You'll be okay now," whispered Action Man, stroking one of the cat's silky soft ears.

Leaving the Snow Leopard to recover, Action Man pounded on up the steep mountain.

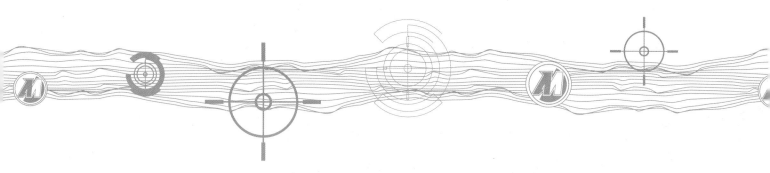

"I bet Gangrene set that trap," he said out loud, gritting his teeth with fury. "He'd like to capture that beautiful animal and turn it into some kind of vicious monster."

"How right you are, Action Man!" laughed Gangrene.

The evil Professor was waiting for his enemy on a narrow ledge.

Before Action Man knew what was happening, Gangrene bounded over and gave him a push in the chest.

"Goodbye, old chap!" laughed the scientist, watching Action Man falling off the ledge.

"I calculate it'll be about sixty second before you smash to pieces on the rocks below. So enjoy the last minute of your life!"

As Action Man turned a somersault in the cold, thin air, the ripcord on the side of his backpack pulled itself automatically.

" Altitude Attack deployed!" he murmured, bracing himself for the jerk as the huge parachute billowed out of the pack and opened above his head like a gigantic flower.

Soon, Action Man was drifting gently downwards towards a flat area of rock.

He landed safely and began to fold up his parachute. It was then that he heard the rumbling!

"You won't escape me again!" roared Gangrene, rolling some heavy boulders down the mountainside. Action Man dodged them, skipping left and right like someone playing a playground game. He thought he was safe when a final boulder brushed past his head, knocking him to the ground.

"Where am I?" groaned Action Man, groggily.

Gangrene was on him like a flash!

"This is it, Action Man!" he shrieked, putting his foul-smelling hands round his rival's throat and starting to squeeze with an iron-like grip. Action Man began to splutter and choke. It seemed as if the mission was over.

Then a friend came to the rescue. With a furious roar, the Snow Leopard leapt down from a rock on top of Gangrene. One swipe of the cat's huge paw sent the Professor reeling backwards. Then a sight of the animal's huge teeth sent the coward fleeing down the mountain!

"I'll get rid of you another day, Action Man!" he shrieked.

It was now starting to get dark and Action Man still needed to locate the mountain cave.

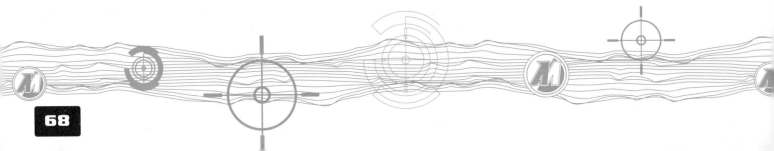

He need not have worried – the Ounce led him straight to it!

"So the cave is your lair, eh?" chuckled Action Man, taking the diamond from the Jungle Zone out of his pocket.

As he approached the cave, a small rock inside began to pulse with light. Action Man exchanged it for his diamond and hurried off down the mountainside, knowing he had taken another step towards unlocking the door to X-City and the Death Ray threatening the world.

"Goodbye, my friend," called Action Man, waving to the Snow Leopard. "Thank you for making me welcome in the Kingdom of The Cat!"

Profile...
ANTI-FREEZE

IN THE FROZEN WASTES OF THE ICE ZONE ON ISLAND X, A CREATURE HAS BEEN TRAPPED IN A BLOCK OF ICE FOR CENTURIES. NOW RELEASED, HE SEEKS TO DESTROY EVERYTHING IN HIS PATH WITH HIS AWESOME ICE-COLD POWERS...

SO FAR, THIS MUCH IS KNOWN ABOUT DR X'S LATEST ALLY –

* Really Cool Customer

ANTI-FREEZE IS NOT JUST COLD-BLOODED. HE HAS SUPER-COOLED *GLYCOL FOR HIS BLOOD. THAT MEANS HE CAN ENDURE THE MOST EXTREME COLD – EVEN ABSOLUTE ZERO (MINUS 273 DEGREES) – WITHOUT EVEN FEELING CHILLY!

*A THICK COLOURLESS LIQUID USED AS AN ANTI-FREEZE

* Frozen Touch

JUST BY BRUSHING THEIR SKIN, ANTI-FREEZE CAN PARALYSE HIS VICTIMS BY MAKING THEM SO COLD THEY CANNOT MOVE A MUSCLE.

* Ice Club

ANTI-FREEZES DEADLY WEAPON IS AN ICE CLUB MADE OF COMPRESSED ICE CRYSTALS. IT IS SO HARD, IT CAN SHATTER HUGE ROCKS - BUT WILL NEVER BREAK ITSELF.

* Hard Man

THANKS TO A BODY MADE OF PURE PACK-ICE, ANTI-FREEZE IS AS HARD AS NAILS. HIS FROZEN BODY CAN TAKE BLOW AFTER BLOW WITHOUT FEELING THE SLIGHTEST THING!

Finally, Dr X has told Anti-Freeze to destroy Action Man on sight. Now there's a **CHILLING** thought!

MISSION BRIEF

In 36 hours, Island X
will be in range of all
the world's major cities.
The Death Ray must be
stopped!

An ice crystal
is located in a frozen
river of ice.

You must obtain it if
you are going to get
into X-City.

ICE ZONE

Location -
AT THE END OF THE SOUTH
EASTERN TIP OF ISLAND X.

Nearest zones -
X-CITY

Known Defences -
THE ZONE IS PROTECTED BY A
HIGH-TECH LASER NET. THE AREA
IS ALSO SEETHING WITH DR X'S
HIGHLY TRAINED SNOW COMMANDOS
AND GENETICALLY ENGINEERED
POLAR BEARS.

Temperature -
A MIND-NUMBING, LIP-CRACKING,
TEETH-CHATTERING MINUS 10 TO
MINUS 20 DEGREES CELSIUS

Special features -
THIS ZONE IS THE HOME OF DR X'S
LATEST ALLY, THE HORRIFIC ICE
MONSTER CALLED ANTI-FREEZE!

MISSION DATA-EQUIPMENT

Polar Trapper

* Specially designed rifle firing twin rockets with a net attachment. The two rockets launch at exactly the same time and fly parallel to one another, carrying the net between them. Once entangled, an enemy cannot escape.

* The net is made of reinforced fabric that is tear-proof, claw-proof, teeth-proof, flame-proof and freeze-proof. It is one of the strongest fabrics ever made by man.

* The Polar Trapper is fitted with a top-mounted firing sight. As well as directing the path of rockets, it can tell distance from target, wind speed, chill factor and other info. that may affect the accuracy of the shot.

* Action Man's laser-powered goggles enable him to see clearly in the blinding confusion of a blizzard or amidst the dazzling glare of a snow-covered landscape.

* Note the short ski-shoes. These rugged. ultra-tough boots with their lightweight metal surrounds are a cunning cross between snow-shoes and skis. Action Man can use them to walk over frozen ground or to ski down the mountainside at breakneck speed like a champion at the Winter Olympics.

* Shoulder-mounted bazooka rocket delivers an extra knockout punch.

FINAL DESTINATION PUZZLE

Requesting Mission Assistance!

ACTION MAN MUST FIND THE ICE-CRYSTAL AT THE FROZEN RIVER OF ICE. WHAT IS THE PROPER NAME FOR THIS PLACE?
HELP ACTION MAN NARROW DOWN HIS DESTINATION BY SOLVING THIS PUZZLE. YOU HAVE TO CHANGE ONE WORD INTO ANOTHER BY ADDING A LETTER AT THE FRONT. USE THE CLUES TO FIND OUT WHAT THE NEW WORDS SHOULD BE AND WRITE THE EXTRA LETTER IN THE BOXES AT THE FRONT.
WHEN YOU HAVE FINISHED, THE LETTERS IN THE BOXES, READING DOWNWARDS, WILL SPELL OUT WHERE ACTION MAN IS HEADING. TO MAKE HIS FINAL EXCHANGE.

Clues:

1. Get bigger
2. Touch down in an aeroplane
3. Seed of the oak tree
4. Squeeze and destroy
5. Heavy metal
6. Bite, chew and swallow
7. Talk and shout very angrily

1. ☐ ROW
2. ☐ AND
3. ☐ CORN
4. ☐ RUSH
5. ☐ RON
6. ☐ AT
7. ☐ ANT

Answers: 1. GROW 2. LAND 3. ACORN 4. CRUSH 5. IRON 6. EAT 7. RANT Action Man's final exchange destination is a GLACIER

SKIING THE AVALANCHE

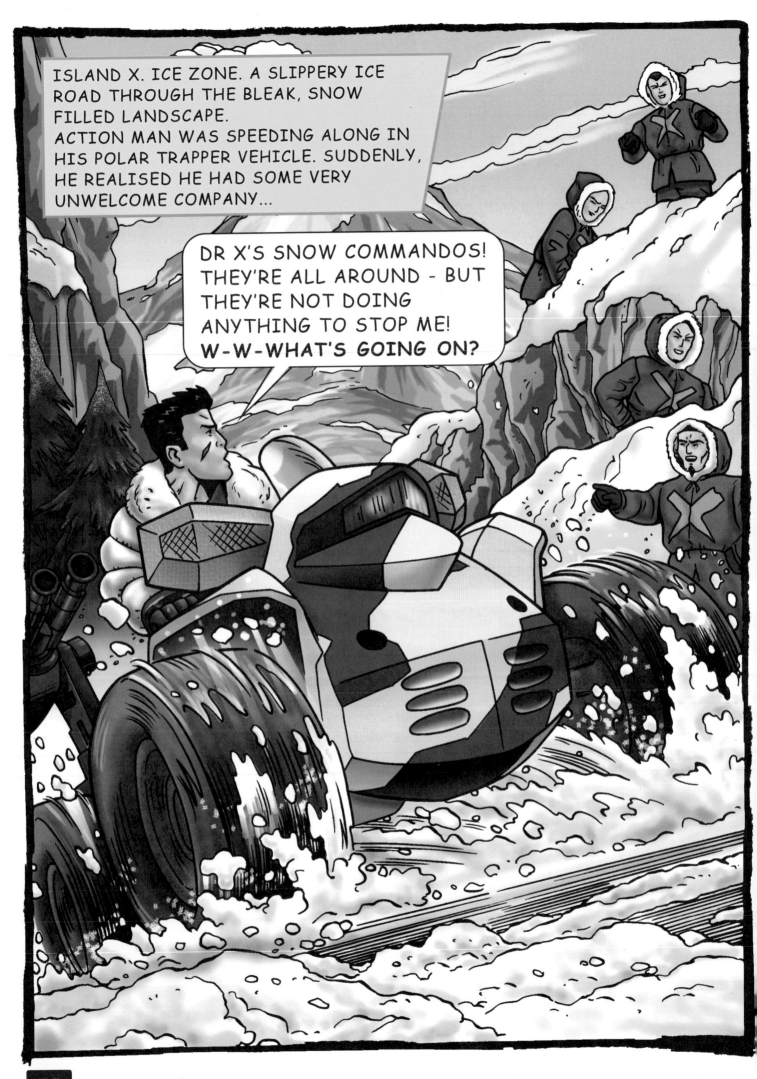

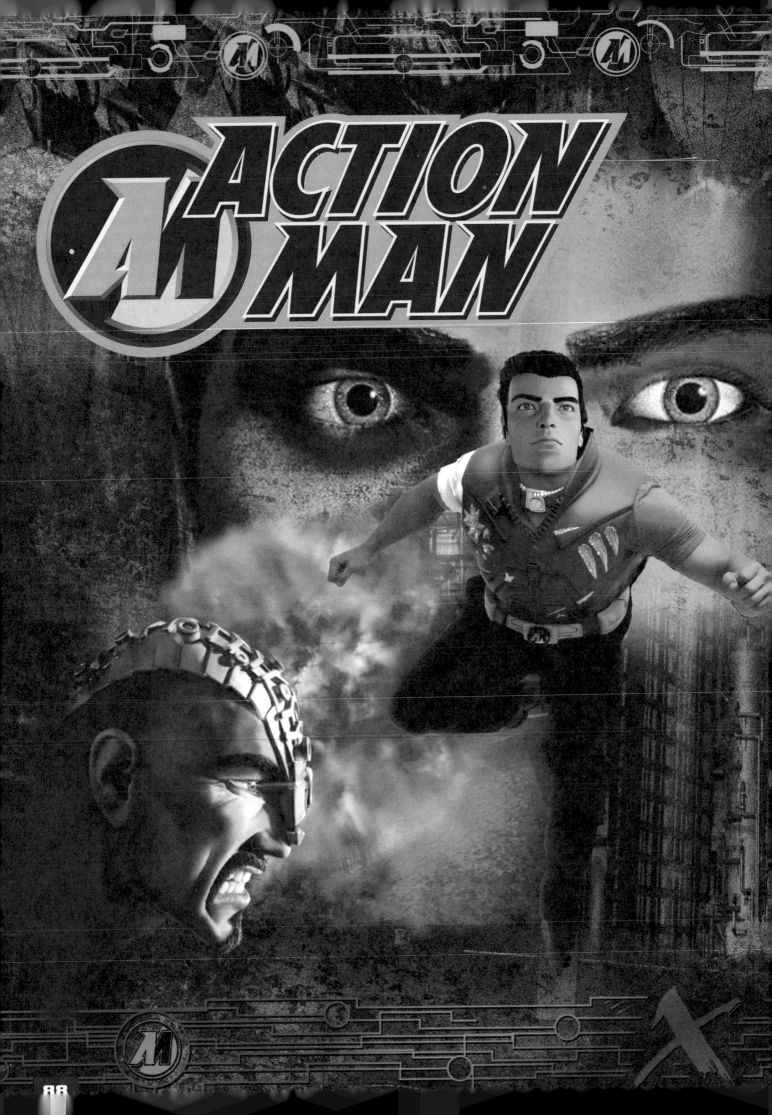

Profile... PROF. GANGRENE

YEUCH!

HOLD YOUR NOSES AS YOU READ THIS PROFILE OF DR X'S LONGEST SERVING HENCHMAN. THE STENCH MIGHT MAKE YOU SICK...

BACKGROUND

PROFESSOR GANGRENE HAS BEEN WITH DR X FOR A LONG TIME. IN HIS YOUTH, THE PROFESSOR STUDIED MICROBIOLOGY – THE SCIENCE OF GERMS, VIRUSES AND OTHER TINY BUGS. THEN HE TOOK PART IN A DANGEROUS EXPERIMENT WHICH WENT HORRIBLY WRONG. AS A RESULT, GANGRENE'S BODY IS FULL OF A REVOLTING, POISONOUS GUNGE THAT GIVES HIM HIS DISGUSTING GREEN COLOUR AND FOUL SMELL.

SPECIAL POWERS

GANGRENE'S TOXIC GUNGE CAN SHRIVEL UP AND DESTROY ANY LIVING MATTER THAT IT TOUCHES. SO THE PROFESSOR USES IT AS A WEAPON, FIRING A STREAM OF THE DEADLY JELLY TO ELIMINATE ANYONE OR ANYTHING IN HIS PATH. HIS GHASTLY DESTRUCTIVE POWER MAKES HIM ONE OF THE WORLD'S BIGGEST THREATS TO THE ENVIRONMENT.

GANGRENE CONTINUES TO CONDUCT EXPERIMENTS THAT WILL HELP DR X IN HIS QUEST FOR WORLD DOMINATION.

MISSION BRIEF

Since arriving on the island, the underwater volcano has speeded up the movement of Island X. It will now be in range of all major cities in only 6 hours. Enter X-City, access Dr X's base and destroy the Death Ray.
Go for Broke!

CITY AND X'S BASE

Location -
X-CITY IS AT THE CENTRE OF ISLAND X... AND X'S BASE IS IN THE CENTRE OF THE CITY!

Nearest zones -
JUNGLE, ICE AND EXTREME MOUNTAIN

Known Defences -
X-CITY IS PROTECTED BY THREE WIRE FENCES, EACH ONE HIGHER AND TOUGHER THAN THE ONE BEFORE. X'S BASE CAN ONLY BE ENTERED BY CRACKING THE SECRET CODE THAT OPENS THE DOOR.

Temperature -
FLUCTUATES WILDLY BETWEEN EXTREME HOT AND COLD DUE TO HIGH POLLUTION LEVELS

Special features -
THE DOME-SHAPED CEILING OF X'S BASE OPENS TO ALLOW THE BEAM OF THE DEATH RAY TO BE FIRED UPWARDS.

93

MISSION DATA-EQUIPMENT

Raid 4x4 -

* CHUNKY FOUR-WHEEL DRIVE VEHICLE CAPABLE OF ULTRA HIGH SPEEDS IN ANY TYPE OF CITY ENVIRONMENT.
* PAINTED WITH THE SAME SPECIAL BLACK PAINT AS THE LATEST HIGH-TECH STEALTH BOMBERS AND ATTACK SHIPS.
* THE ENGINE IS AN AWESOME FIVE-LITRE 16 VALVE V-8 THAT DELIVERS ENOUGH POWER TO DRIVE A CAR THREE TIMES THE SIZE.
* THE TYRES ARE ADAPTED FROM FORMULA ONE MOTOR RACING TYRES, COMBINING SUPER-FAST SPEED WITH TOTAL GRIP IN ALL WEATHERS. THEY ARE ALSO PUNCTURE-PROOF AND WILL REMAIN INFLATED EVEN WHEN THEY HAVE A HOLE IN THEM THANKS TO A UNIQUE SELF-REPAIRING LAYER JUST BELOW THE TREAD.
* THE 4X4 IS SPECIALLY ADAPTED TO CARRY ACTION MAN'S DOG, RAID. THIS HIGHLY TRAINED AND SUPER-INTELLIGENT ANIMAL IS ENORMOUSLY STRONG AND CAPABLE OF LEAPING BREATH TAKING-HEIGHTS.

Street Biker –

* Action Man's all-powerful Street Biker was designed by a team of the world's leading mountain bike manufacturers, combining the best features of all their models in one ultimate super-bike.
* Top speed - a staggering 80 miles per hour!
* The unique pedal action and built-in gears mean the Street Biker requires little effort to ride, but can go from standing still to 60 mph in less than 15 seconds - that's faster than many cars!
* Street Biker is equipped with a forward-firing rocket mounted just below the handlebars. Released at the push of a button, this deadly weapon is capable of removing any obstacle in the road ahead.
* The suspension forks, mounted on both front and back wheels, can take any amount of punishment and give a smooth, comfortable ride even over the roughest ground.
* Action Man never rides without his cycle helmet which is made of lightweight, ultra-tough fibreglass with a clear plastic visor. He also carries a full toolbox to enable running repairs to be made whenever they are needed.

CRACK THE COLOUR CODE

Requesting Mission Assistance!

THE THREE OBJECTS THAT ACTION MAN FOUND ON ISLAND X ARE ALL-IMPORTANT.
THEY WILL ENABLE HIM TO SELECT THE CORRECT COLOUR CODE TO ENTER X'S BASE.
HELP ACTION MAN TO FIND THE RIGHT COLOUR BY SOLVING THE RIDDLE BELOW. EACH LINE MENTIONS ONE OBJECT ALONG WITH SOME OTHER WORDS. STUDY THEM CAREFULLY AND PICK OUT ONE LETTER THAT OCCUR IN ALL THREE WORDS. THEN WRITE THESE LETTERS IN THE BOX AT THE BOTTOM TO SPELL OUT THE VITAL COLOUR.

a) My first is in CRYSTAL, in Rice and in REAR,

b) My second's in CAVE, in Egg and in EAR,
My third is in DIAMOND, in DOOR and in DEAR!

What colour am I?

SHOWDOWN IN X-CITY

TELLING RAID TO WAIT FOR HIS RETURN, ACTION MAN MADE STRAIGHT FOR A HUGE STEEL DOOR IN THE MAIN BUILDING. THERE WAS NOT A SECOND TO WASTE, **BUT...**

ALL THESE COLOURS ARE FLASHING VERY FAST. I'VE GOT TO PRESS THE RIGHT COLOUR AT THE RIGHT TIME TO GET IN!

WAIT FOR IT...WAIT FOR IT... **NOW!**

WHIRR!

PHEW! DONE IT! HATE TO THINK WHAT WOULD HAVE HAPPENED IF I'D PRESSED THE WRONG ONE!

107

MISSION DEBRIEFING

HIS JOB DONE FOR THE TIME BEING, ACTION MAN HAS ONE FINAL TASK TO PERFORM BEFORE HE CAN TAKE A WELL EARNED BREAK. HE HAS TO REPORT BACK ON EVERYTHING THAT'S HAPPENED.

THE TROUBLE IS ... SO MUCH HAPPENED IN SO SHORT A TIME, HE CANNOT REMEMBER IT ALL!

CAN YOU HELP HIM? ANSWER THE VARIOUS QUESTIONS ABOUT THE FIVE MISSIONS ON ISLAND X.

FINALLY, A WORD TO YOU FROM ACTION MAN HIMSELF – "THANK YOU FOR ALL YOUR MISSION ASSISTS, SPECIAL AGENTS!"

http://www.actionman.com

Mission One – OCEAN ZONE

1 ACTION MAN WAS ATTACKED BY TWO DIFFERENT TYPES OF SHARK AS HE SWAM TOWARDS ISLAND X. ONE WAS A GREAT WHITE SHARK. WHAT WAS THE OTHER TYPE CALLED?

A) HAMMERHEAD   B) BLOCKHEAD   C) PINHEAD

2 COMPLETE THE MISSING WORD TO SAY WHAT CAUSED THE GIGANTIC TIDAL WAVE THAT CARRIED ACTION MAN TO THE ISLAND.

UNDERWATER V

3 WHAT WAS THE SURFING TERM USED TO DESCRIBE FALLING OFF YOUR SURFBOARD?

A) WIPE-DOWN   B) BABY-WIPE   C) WIPE-OUT

Mission Two – JUNGLE ZONE

4 WHAT DID ACTION MAN USE TO JUMP OUT OF THE WAY OF THE AZTEC WARRIORS' SPEARS?

A) A ROPE   B) A TREE CREEPER   C) A TRAMPOLINE

5 WHICH ONE OF DR X'S HORRIBLE FRIENDS WAS HIDING IN A TOMB INSIDE THE PYRAMID?

6 THE VALUABLES INSIDE THE PYRAMID WERE PROTECTED BY LOTS

Mission Three – EXTREME MOUNTAIN ZONE

7   ON THE LOWER SLOPES, WHAT KIND OF BEARS ATTACKED ACTION MAN?

  A) BROWN BEARS   B) POLAR BEARS   C) TEDDY BEARS

8   WHEN ACTION MAN'S LAST SNOW DISC WAS DAMAGED, IT FLEW LIKE A BOOMERANG. FILL IN THE MISSING LETTERS TO SAY WHICH COUNTRY BOOMERANGS COME FROM.

A _ _ **T** _ _ _ _ **A**

3   WHAT IS THE PROPER NAME FOR THE SNOW LEOPARD THAT RESCUED ACTION MAN AND LED HIM TO THE HIDDEN CAVE?

  A) OUNCE   B) GRAMME   C) TON

Mission Four – ICE ZONE

10 WHAT TYPE OF NET GUARDS THIS ZONE?

  A) FISHING NET   B) LASER NET   C) HAIR NET

11 ANTI-FREEZE HAS GLYCOL INSTEAD OF BLOOD TO PREVENT HIM FROM FREEZING EVEN IN THE COLDEST CONDITIONS.

  A) TRUE   B) FALSE

12 HOW DID ACTION MAN BRING ON THE AVALANCHE THAT ALLOWED HIM TO ESCAPE?

Mission Five – X CITY AND BASE ZONE

13 WHAT IS THE NAME OF ACTION MAN'S DOG?

14 HOW DID ACTION MAN GET PAST THE GUARDS AT THE ENTRANCE TO X'S BASE?

  A) HE SNEAKED PAST THEM
  B) HE ASKED POLITELY IF HE COULD COME IN.
  C) HE FIRED THE ROCKET ON THE FRONT OF HIS STREET BIKE.

15 HOW DID ACTION MAN LEAVE ISLAND X AT THE END OF HIS FINAL MISSION?

  A) BY PLANE   B) BY HELICOPTER   C) BY BUS

Answers: 1. a) Hammerhead 2. VOLCANO 3. c) Wipe-out 4. b) Tree-creeper 5. Professor Gangrene 6. b) False (It is booby-trapped) 7. b) Polar Bears 8. AUSTRALIA 9. a) Ounce 10. b) Laser net 11. a) True 12. He shouted loudly 13. Raid 14. c) He fired the rocket on the front of his Street Bike 15. b) By helicopter

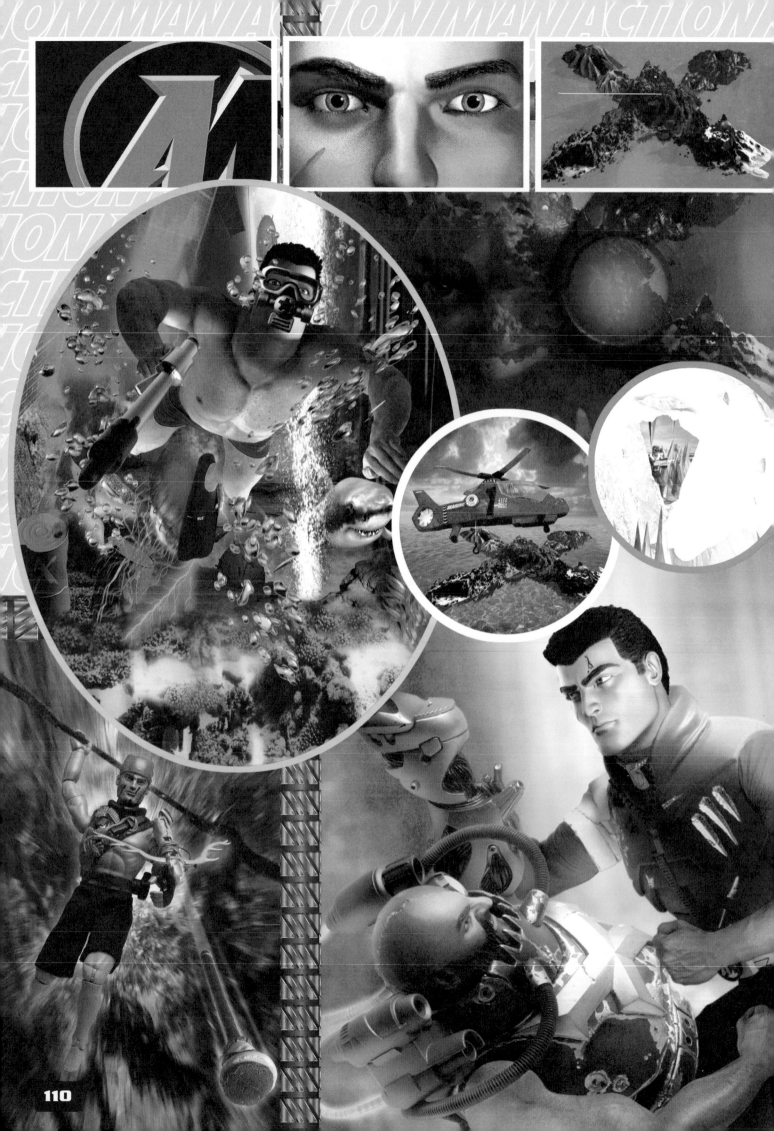